Illustrated by Pete Avdoulos, Mark Busacca, Emi Fukawa, Victor Lee, Wendy K. Lee, Douglas Scott, Peggy Smith, Alexandr Stolin, Vadim Vahrameev, Hanako Wakiyama, Nelson Wang and Bill Yenne.

Printed in Italy

Series UPC: 39440

Bible Classics

Noah and the Ark

Modern Publishing
A Division of Unisystems, Inc.
New York, New York 10022
Series UPC: 39440

In the years after the time of Adam and Eve and their children, the world had become a troubled place where people disobeyed God's laws.

In this world, there lived a good man named
Noah and his family.

God decided to wash the world clean with a huge Flood. He told Noah that he should save himself and his family by building a large boat called an Ark.

When Noah and his family began to work on the Ark, their neighbors asked them why they were building a huge boat so far from the sea. Noah told them what God had said, but they laughed at him.

At last, the Ark was finished. God told Noah to load the Ark with enough food for his family and for the animals that would be traveling with them.

The first animals to board the Ark may
have been the pet cats and dogs
that lived with Noah's family.

News of the coming Flood spread to all of the creatures in the nearby woods. The squirrels, the bunnies, the birds and even old Mr. and Mrs. Mole heard about it.

The bears and the deer, the raccoons and the owls in the deep forests heard the news. The camels, the buzzards and the lizards, and even the jackals all hurried to Noah's Ark.

Hundreds of animals were streaming to the Ark, two by two.
There were lions and tigers and pandas.

There were cows and zebras. There were turtles and turkeys.
There were snakes and dragonflies.

As the last of the animals scampered aboard, Noah noticed the first raindrops of the storm that God had said would bring the great Flood.

Soon it would be raining harder than it had ever rained before. Noah and his family entered the Ark and God closed the door.

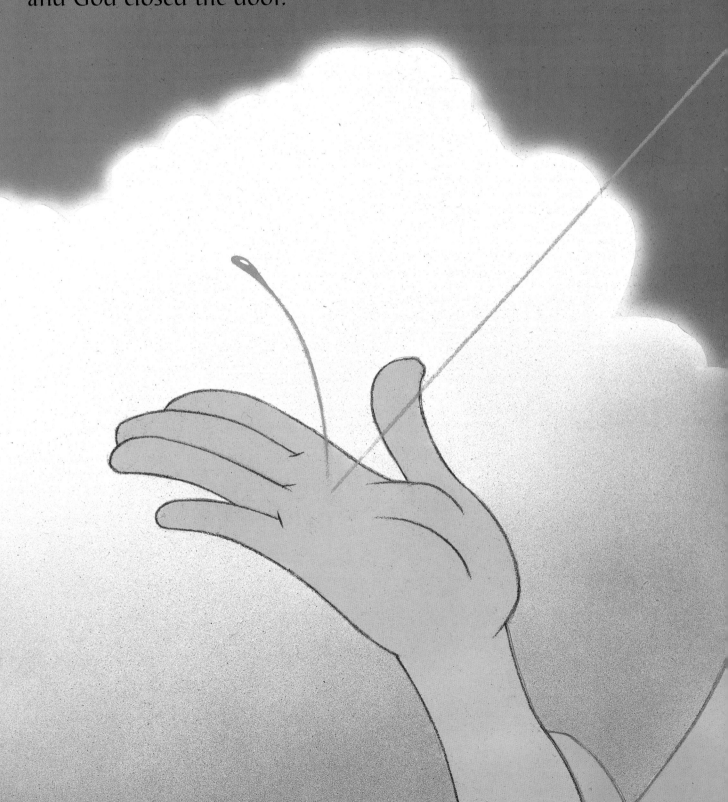

The wind blew and the rain poured. The Flood came, the waters rose, and soon the Ark was floating free.

It rained for forty days and forty nights. At last, God decided that the Earth had been washed clean.

After many days had passed, Noah decided to send a raven out the window to see if there was a dry place for the bird to land. But the raven couldn't find one.

The next day Noah sent a dove out. The dove came back with a green olive branch in her beak. That meant that somewhere plants were starting to grow.

A week later, Noah let the dove go again. This time, the dove didn't return. This meant that the water had gone down and she had found a place to build her nest.

The great Flood was over.

Noah and his family praised God and thanked Him for keeping them safe.

Time passed and the world began to fill with people and animals again. Only this time, it was much more peaceful.

God promised that He would never again flood the whole Earth. To remind everyone of that promise, He made the first rainbow and put it in the sky.

Even now, when we see a rainbow after a storm, we remember God's promise. When we do, we also remember Noah and the Ark.